Farmers
Market
→

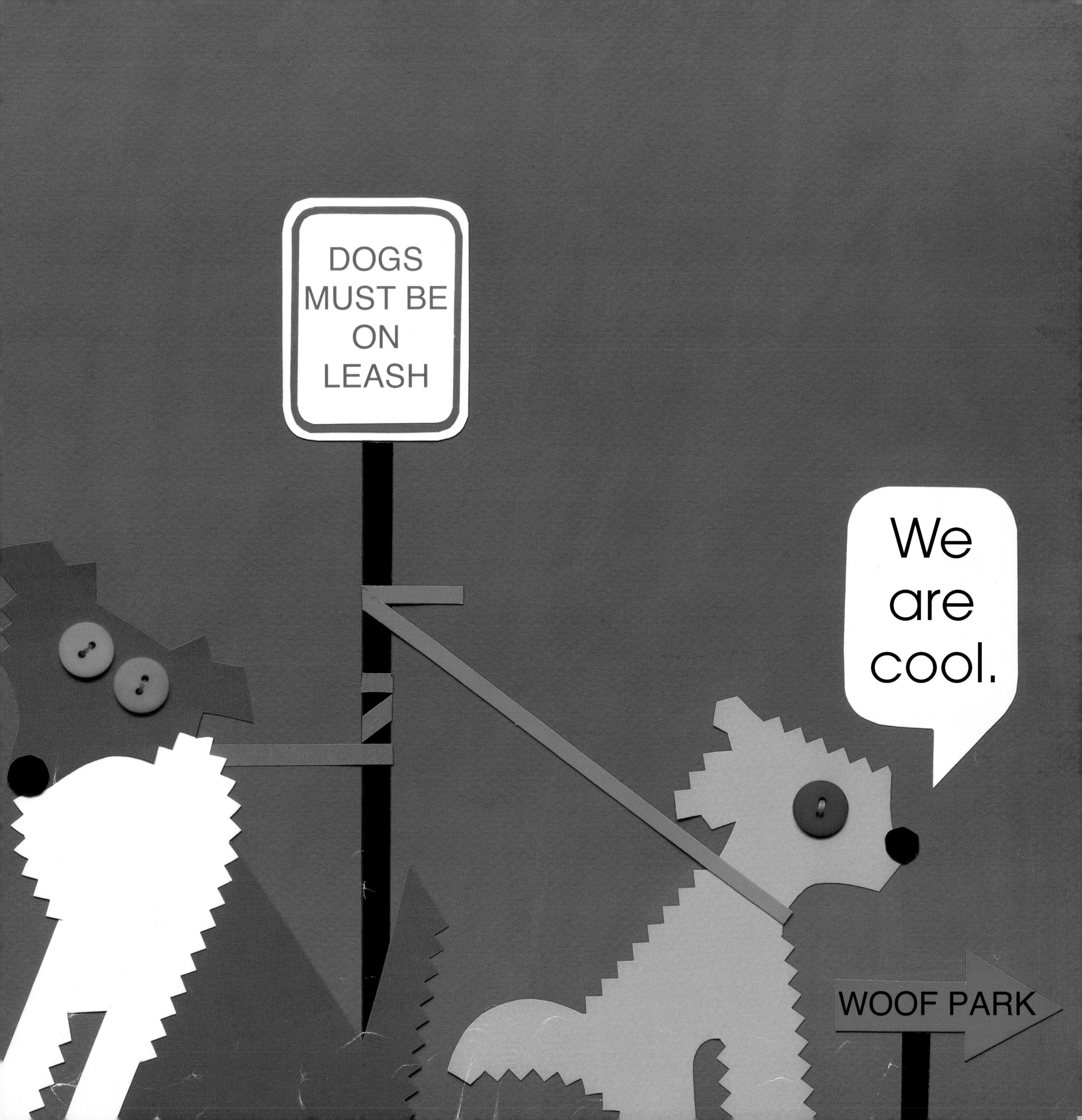
DOGS MUST BE ON LEASH
We are cool.
WOOF PARK

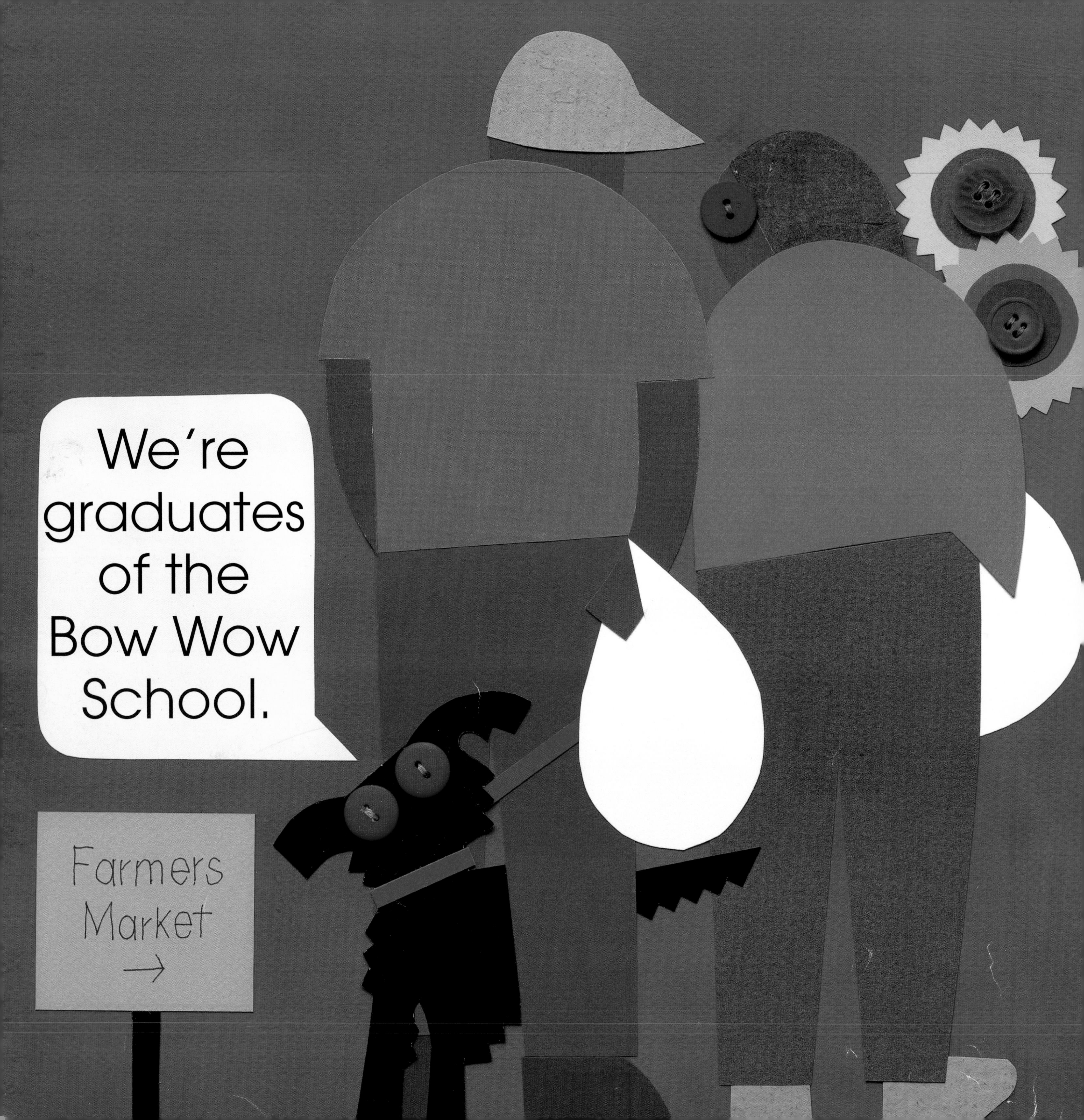
We're graduates of the Bow Wow School.
Farmers Market →

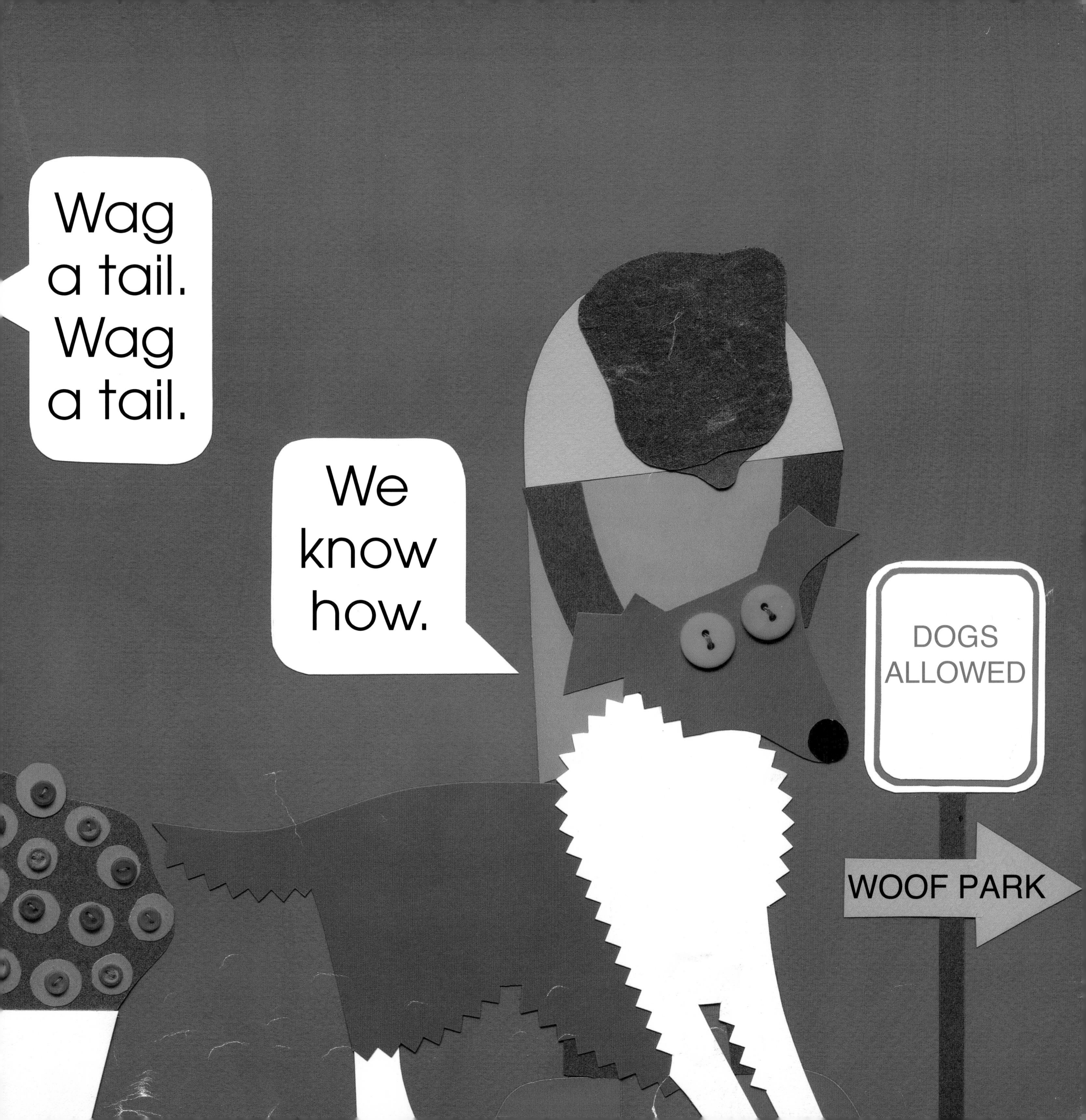
Wag a tail. Wag a tail.
We know how.
DOGS ALLOWED
WOOF PARK

# Bow Wow School Graduates

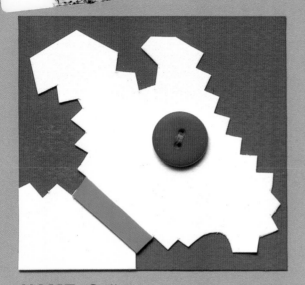

**NAME:** Spike
**FAMILY:** Unknown
Lively, fun loving, high energy. May chase small animals, likes to howl. Keep an eye on Spike, he needs more obedience training.

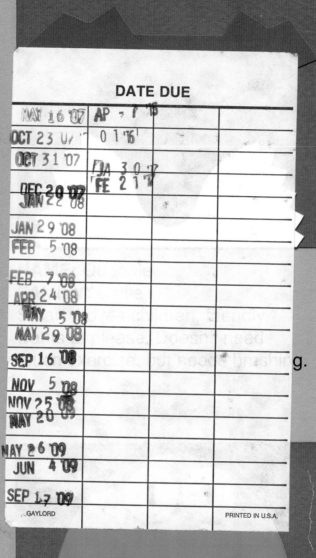

| DATE DUE | | |
|---|---|---|
| MAY 16 07 | AP · 7 '15 | |
| OCT 23 U/ '7 | 0 1 '15' | |
| OCT 31 '07 | JA 3 0 7 | |
| DEC 20 07 | FE 2 1 7 | |
| JAN 22 '08 | | |
| JAN 29 '08 | | |
| FEB 5 '08 | | |
| FEB 7 '08 | | |
| APR 24 '08 | | |
| MAY 5 08 | | |
| MAY 29 08 | | |
| SEP 16 '08 | | |
| NOV 5 08 | | |
| NOV 25 08 | | |
| MAY 20 09 | | |
| MAY 26 09 | | |
| JUN 4 '09 | | |
| SEP 17 09 | | |

GAYLORD                    PRINTED IN U.S.A.

**NAME:** Oscar
**FAMILY:** Dachshund
Loves to be involved in family activities. Clever, but easily bored. Likes city living, enjoys long walks in the park.

**NAME:** Lucky
**FAMILY:** Scottish Terrier (Scottie)
Independent, spunky. Barks a lot, would be a good watchdog. Needs exercise, may chase small animals.

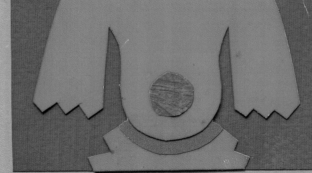

**NAME:** Fluffy
**FAMILY:** Irish Setter
Needs exercise, happy when she can run and play.

**NAME:** Rufus
**FAMILY:** Labrador Retriever
Kind, outgoing, likes to please. Loves to retrieve balls and Frisbee